Short Chapters

From

Sunset

Chris Tutton

First published in the UK by Avalanche Books, England.

Copyright © Chris Tutton 2023.

The right of Chris Tutton to be identified as the author of this work has been asserted by him in accordance with the Copyright, Designs and Patents Act 1988.

British Library Cataloguing in Publication Data.

A catalogue record for this book is available from the British Library.

ISBN: 978 1 874392 20 0

Printed by SRP, Exeter, England.

Contents:

A MOMENT OF MURMURATION

It took a cyclone of stubborn swallows to
fashion summer from a jumble of rain;

uncouple us from our resinous beds of
reed. Above the clouds, we grew feathers

of wind; tumbling and soaring into each
other's drift, like a storm of birdsong.

AN AGE OF REMEMBRANCE

In the monastery of your arms rests a
lawn of braille, where I garden sleep.

By the millhouse of your summer lips
and the breath of your slumber song,

beneath the open parasol of your kiss;
among downy-soft hatchling mornings,

where we seeded ourselves meadows of
wilder flowers; you, musk mallow pink,

shimmering down to the river
in a cloud of wings.

THE FALLOW YIELD

The old man hummed quietly in the cool shade beside a watchtower of sorrow, winding the last burnished yarn of summer onto a skein. In the crowing breeze, tambourine leaves turned slowly to autumn, and sated geese flew swollen into a prodigal spread. The old man paused for a moment, rested his song, and briefly read the gnarled journal of his worn hands as a stranger. 'Soon, the river will flow too fast and become too cold to bathe in', thought the old man, as he felt the soft twine slip through his fingers, 'and I will taste nothing but the flavour of winter.' In the mewing distance, a crimson veined evening purred and bedded unfurled claws into the fraying skyline.

As the old man continued to reflect on the passing season, a white mule laden with apples appeared at his side. The white mule affably extended a cordial salutation, which the old man, although unable to remember any previous encounter with the mule, returned with the warm, easy grace of a fond acquaintance. 'I have often glimpsed you from afar, standing atop the tower, old man,' the mule began, 'and each time have I attempted to understand the purpose of your surveillance.'

The old man would have preferred to remain alone and continue to fix the thread of his broken melody, but he felt awkwardly answerable to the mule's amiable gaze and accordingly scratched his grey bearded chin pensively, allowing himself a few uncomfortable seconds to form his reply.

'Every day, I have climbed this lofty tower and watched, but I am a foolish old man and my vision is dimming. Each sunrise, I see less than I did the sunset before and I watch little but the day receding from my grasp', he lamented, at once feeling ashamed of his complaint.

'What do you wish to see, old man?' the white mule posed, with a sympathetic smile.

'The expected. Or the unexpected. It makes no difference,' sighed the old man, 'what I wish to see I shall not, and I must settle for any view in its absence.'

Crickets clicked chattering heels, and a peal of cattle bells clanged a languid chorus to accompany the late afternoon's slovenly passage.

'Once, I looked out onto a colourful distance, which seemed to stretch endlessly into the blue sky, and everywhere I looked I saw myself threshing grain, herding sheep, fishing clear streams. But now I look upon a distance which has caught up with me and I am unable to find myself there.'

'You hoard your sadness as a sleepless old man gathers over-ripe fruit from the tree of dreams, with no thought for the usefulness of his harvest', the mule advised, shaking its head softly to and fro.

The old man fell silent for a moment and thought hard on the white mule's words.

'My harvest feeds me well enough. I am an old man and I need nothing more than I can take without reaching.'

'You eat the fruit within your reach, yet the fruit is bitter and you complain of its flavour. How does this satisfy you?'

'I am satisfied by the memory of how it once tasted, even though it has become unpalatable to me now.'

'You have grown fat on your sorrow, old man, perhaps you would care to walk with me for a while, and I will show you a sweeter fruit ripe for the picking.'

The old man thanked the mule gratefully, but made no attempt to stand. 'Perhaps I will find a sweeter fruit of my own soon', he mused, as he watched the mule retreat.

'Farewell then, old man,' bid the white mule, turning and beginning to walk slowly away, 'I have a long journey ahead, and I must not delay. But I shall remember you well, and I shall think of you often. And I shall see you always on the prow of an endless distance, regardless of my station, or whatever view lies before me.'

THE LOOP ROUTE

By vespers, we had side-stepped the
doormat dead; danced lazily, dreamy

among the pipistrelles. Following the

slithering sundown of our aimless amble,
the rowdy home-crowd chants of bush-

crickets in the after dinner grass raised our

floundering game, to wish the long night
light enough to see that all we really wanted

was to settle seamlessly into each other and

live, weightless above the graveyard, for
an hour.

A PASSAGE OF INGRESS

We set our little boats on the
drift of this endless turning of
tides. Now

weaving, now touching, now
tumbling on the wandering
sands of

each other; beaches, which,
tomorrow, will be peopled
by strangers.

A PRAYER FOR
THE DAMMED

If I were young and
strong enough to

reach inside this
bygone book of sleep,

I'd sweep my brabbled
memories clean and

trade with such exquisite
dreams these

flotsam days of
careworn wanderings.

EXPERIENCE SHATTERS OUR ILLUSIONS BUT COMPELS US TO FOREVER COLLECT THE FRAGMENTS OF THEIR REMAINS

In the swallowing thirst of solitude,
we remain tantalised by
echoes of water.

THREE HAIKU
(MINUS TWO)

When she touches him,
he will almost remember
the weight of his hands.

A VAIN PURSUIT

I imagined I could
chase you
further than I
could run. You out-

paced me, leaving
me clutching
the scent of
your departure.

CODA NOSTRUM

We misappropriate
curative provisions
from apparitional farm-
steads of insomnolence;

devour them alive in kill-
cold, canary yellow corn-
stick corrals of dawn,
famished as alley cats.

IN THE BEGINNING, WE REFUSED
TO BELIEVE THAT OLD AGE
WOULD NOT ANNOUNCE ITSELF
UPON ITS ARRIVAL, BUT IT HAD
BEEN A GUEST IN OUR HOUSE
LONG BEFORE EITHER OF US
REALISED THAT IT WAS THERE.
WE EXCUSED IT TO OUR FRIENDS
AND MADE ALLOWANCES FOR ITS
GAUCHE MANNERISMS, BUT IT
TOOK INCREASING EXCEPTION
TO WHAT IT CONSIDERED TO BE
OUR PATRONISING ATTITUDE
AND THREATENED TO KILL US

It was only within our transitory
moments of uncertainty that

we became aware of even
greater things to be

unsure of.

A MOMENTARY EPOCH OF APPREHENSION

He bows into your gaze,
a little cautious of your

eye. The butterfly wing
of your passing cheek

just close enough to be
crushed by a footstep.

SOMETIMES THERE WERE TIMES WHEN THE TIMES THEMSELVES SEEMED TIMELESS

...and we wish now that we had
snatched them up as anxious
mothers; clutched their sweet
secrets in our arms, needled
the colours of them into our
frames as more than pictures.

Wish that we had not lowered
our eyes from them so gullibly,
nor permitted them to be drawn
from us so cheaply into the swim,
to drown in icy waters of such
unimaginably distant lands.

A VERY NEARLY INADVERTENTLY UNREQUITED FULL THREE ACTS OF CALAMITOUS RECONCILIATION

In the quietus of this night, we must
forsake our yield. Surrender our
turning leaves to the wind. You will

squeeze my hand gently with your far-
away eyes, sing something, sotto voce,
sweet, warm as a tear. And I will need to

find myself among you somewhere: angle
my deafness towards the trailing, inky
nimbus of your verse, just far enough

away from its sleepless thunder to
hear you breathe, sail, over the shifting
sands of my incurably inconsonant reply.

A PEACE SO CLOSE TO COMFORT

Somewhere, in the hidden
metaphor on the stave, the

double-dogged Golgotha of the
day, adrift, unanchored from his

brood, his black eye turned inside
himself to roost amid the billowing

apron of her tree; the gravity of his

sleep weightless beneath her kiss,
his broken brushes, her fresh green

leaves stuffed like quills into
the thinning branches

of his sky.

THE COUNT

All gifts of beauty now
departed, in sand-eyed,
lamplit

bare-knuckled bend of
day. Childless,
uncomfortable,

pillowed on the bell,
losing the count of
magpie

memories; a familiar
stranger, unready for
the ring.

MYTHOLOGY IS THE
MOTHER TONGUE
OF TYRANNY

The past has arrived
too late for us to

profit from it now; the
eye of the storm is

already full of tears.

THE BIRTH OF REBIRTH

I have arrived once again at
the point of my departure;
a sempiternal silkworm,

interminably attempting to
perfect my flight from the
calaboose of my cocoon.

THE SUTURE OF ANCIENT WOUNDS

We twine estival memories
into the noose of a needle,

thimble up the knee; stitch
our fugitive colours to

graceless, sackcloth, rush-
light weeds of winter.

STORM DAMAGE TO BEDROOM CEILING

Twelve gauge needles of
Art Blakey
thunder into my repose,

tattooing rimshots on
Akstafa skins between
incommodious dreams.

THE TOUCH

We became,
above

the axis of flesh,
beneath lilac and rain,

in silken arcs of sighs,
a touch;

the endless orbit of
a kiss.

THE ADORNMENT

'I am learning
to pluck the
pearl from

the opening
shell of
every new

day', sighed
Martha,
stringing a

necklace of
optimism too
delicate to wear.

WHILE OLD MEN
BATHED IN
RIVERS OF RAIN

We gathered wisps of
fleece from twisted

barbs on invisible
palings, which had

only recently been
erected to remind us

that impudent sheep
had trespassed against

us and stolen all our
woolly coats we had so

meticulously maintained
for the winter.

AN UNEXPECTED CHRISTMAS PRESENT AND THE CONSEQUENT DAWN OF A BEAUTIFUL NEW FRIENDSHIP

But for an innocent
slip of the tongue,

you may only ever
have given me socks.

AUTEUR'D STATES OF CONSCIOUSNESS

Mise-en-sène is constructed from
a collage of incomprehension.
You saunter on set, unsure of your
mark, reading cues from the

disguised eye of my mistimed
arrival, whilst casting me inaudible
lines from a compendium of
catastrophically unscripted movies.

STUPIDITY IS THE WORK OF IDIOTS

'I would prefer to
consider myself,'

sighed Nigel,
attempting to

mortise a square
aphorism into

a circular whole,
'as the discerning

person's lapse in
concentration.'

HOLIDAY ROUTE TO SOMEWHERE BEYOND THE IMPERFECT PERIMETER OF POLEMICS

We drove
all through
the night,

from familiarity
to contempt;
not even

slackening our
career before
the redlights.

THE BECKONING

You invite me to
perform
in the arena of

your eyes,

clenching a
sheltered
breath to

your chest.

Your smile
lingers:
an uncertain

applause, then

wavers like
the fingers of
a cornfield.

A LONG DRIFT BACK TO THE SKY

In the amber of the hour, pearly
curtains fly half-mast on
shallow sighs of autumn. The

wax moon of your cheekbone
yellows.

In weeping gardens, we
peck like sparrows at
the crumbs of your breath;

drown and drift on impossible
waves, infinitesimal tides;

sail the midnight ferry of your
fingers to unimaginable islands,
where desolate, curious children

await memories of sunset on this
dreadful Season of Forgetfulness.

FALTERING REFRAIN

cultivated the music of

from the instruments

thought Martha,

attempting to sing without

the moment.

I have

angels

of silence

anxiously

breaking

STYGIAN SHORE

I watch you from the
beach of dreams,
moonlit on

feldspar crags,
where
quiet breezes keep

your bronze tresses
lapping your neck
like a midnight tide.

ASPHODEL

With the liniment of
this brush, I could
pronounce your
presence with a

carnival of colour;
elevate you forever
beyond the inscription
of my name; bloom

the violet-scented
roses in your garden
and land petals of
daylight onto

your sleep; raise the
long drawn drapery
of your cloud-cloaked
eyelids with a kiss.

HONEYSUCKLE

I am wreathed on the
trellis of your subterfuge,
a ring spun yarn, a stick-

fingered drowning, a
spaghetti-veined
drifting derelict from

a raft of rattletrap
promises, mid-wintered;
frost-hardened, tied-in,

lime-bound to a rubble of
desire that I bloom here;
festoon this frigid brick-

dust bower unmatched,
if not immaculate, with a
flourish brighter than night.

I TOOK YOU TO THE MOST ROMANTIC SUBTEXT IN THE WORLD AND YOU DIDN'T EVEN RECOGNISE THE LANDMARKS.

Perhaps I should have held you a little tighter
in the slip joint pliers of my palm when I
pulled you like a tooth into the mullioned rain;

dried you off, rubbed you down, reconstructed
you as Odile and cantered you through evening
pristine pearly Louvre limbs warm and young.

Maybe I should have confessed something kind,
cinematically confidential; vestured you as idol
when your movie turned monochrome against

me, lighting me dark in sickly silver motor-moon-
shine grey, panning me as I ran to keep pace with
the shot, past poignantly polyphonic choral even-

song sots, staggering side-men to the whistling
wind, over-blowing offbeat all the way down the
ineffable burden of the Boulevard Saint Michel.

THE PIPER

I inflate you with the
bellows of my sorrow,

gild you with the
intangible gold of

dreams; play you
over and over as

you recede, note by
note, release you into

darkness from the
unfastening grasp of

my kiss; the lantern
of your laughter, the

opium of your smile,
the sacred lifeblood of

your love, ink on
my pages.

THE SOCRATIC METHOD

I optimistically proposed that
the apparently unbridgeable

gulf between our problematic
perspectives was merely an

awkwardly unresolved issue
of neglected dialectics.

Your diversivolent eyebrow
briefly considered my hopeful

hypothesis, then dismissively
informed me that I was wrong.

THE TRANSCENDENCE
OF SUNRISE

I miss the play of your light
upon my shadow and stone,

where I dream of undiscovered
apostrophes. Your diaphanous

hedgerow looms, the empyreal
filament of daybreak; lustrous

drawstrings you still
weave for twilight's skyline.

HALCYON MORNING

Those were the days,
when we could

sit on the

crenellated railway
bridge, high above

the tracks,

taking in the sun and
not even thinking

of jumping.

**YOU OFFERED ME YOUR
LOVE AS AN IMPOSSIBLE
EXCHANGE. I ACCEPTED
IT WITH APPREHENSION,
AS A MORSEL TOO
DELICATE TO SKEWER
WITH A PITCHFORK.**

When spiralling inflation rendered
the maintenance of our unavailing

investment unconscionable, we
papered over widening cracks

in our bastions of acrimony with
the old newsprint of accusatory

glances. Neither of us convinced
that we could ever fully commit

to the incalculable expense of
permanently dropping our gaze.

A DAY OF JUDGEMENT

The small boy offered his father a posy of beguiling
contemplations from an unfolding wasteland of
opinions that he had yet to successfully cultivate.
'Which should be my favourites, Father?' he mused,
excitedly attempting to sniff out the subtleties of
difference between them.
His father accepted the bouquet gently, and carefully
arranged the blooms of the small boy's discourse into a
garbling babble of bouncing balls, with which the small
boy immediately engaged; talking hurriedly in reply to,
and continuing to bounce as quickly as he could.
'But how does this answer my question?' implored the
small boy after a short time, unable to contain his
confusion and already beginning to tire. 'I am no longer
able to keep them all bouncing, or even continue to
hear what they are saying to me. Could you not turn
them into sand, so that I may lay easily upon them and
quietly enjoy the bed of them beneath me?'
His father raised a ruminative eyebrow and lowered
his gaze to meet the confounded face of his faltering
offspring.
'If you wish to rest easily on your contemplations, my

son, your favourites will be those which enable you to sleep. And if your intention is to sleep comfortably on your bed of thoughts, your contemplations will never be more than dreams.'

CONFORMITY BURIED HER ALIVE WITHIN PLAIN SIGHT OF AMBITION

You journey a little
shorter now, trailing

your shadow; hauling
the lumber of your

tapering beauty like
a saddling of scars.

AN IMMEASURABLE HORIZON

We skipped entire chapters to
arrive here, appendices to a
battlefield of pages. Thumbing

memories of a reconstructed
past; improvising codas of ill-
conceived comfort. Meandering

through metaphor to perceive
a consonance in the unequivocal
double-stopping of these cadenzas.

VISTA

From here, the view extends
to nightfall. Curious

ramblers saunter, tracing
these worn tracts of

hollow earth, like
ancient arms

weary of stretching
for beauty.

THE RAIN
MAKER

Sometimes,
beneath

watery skies,
there are

days
when

all lovers
have parted.

THE ASYLUM OF VENUS

I discovered you roosting on the
pitch of my rafters, nesting in

the sway of wandering dreams;

my absent kisses ferrying you,
softly as the wind, without even

stirring the camber of your curls.

THE RESISTANCE OF MEMORY

We could live so well then, in the
cavernous emptiness of each
other's words; spend idyllic

holidays beached on subterfuge,
wade out of our depth in clear
blue water. We could render the

render of our evenings nourishing
then, in luminant cracks of
perception spilling reflections

onto the polished half-full glass
of things we hadn't said; scarcely
fluorescent enough to notice

how the torch-light dying lay
strewn around us like summers
buttoned up to the chin.

HIPPOPOTOMONSTROS-ESQUIPPEDALIOPHOBIA

'I have tied myself in knots
with words', sighed Martha,

attempting to free herself from
a captivity of misinterpretation.

A BAPTISMAL DROWNING.
PART 1: THE IMPENDING
IMMERSION

Matilda pulls me closer to water,
little hand
still wet with rain.

A WISTFUL RETREAT

In the flame-marbled morning,
we were always young and wise,

gathering tinder for fiery dreams,
painting each day with a new disguise.

But starker, through the gate of evening,
shirking the staring eye of our sell,

a colder sun strokes shadows on our
ageing skin, like a wave of farewell.

THE APPRENTICE

Little by little, she
mastered the complex

vernacular of
old age; the

exclamatory groan of
wind-shoved timber,

the hopeful stooping
home-coming lunge

to finish by a head.

PROJECTION WHEEL DISASTER

'I just can't get this
image
out of my head',
sighed Norma,
bleeding
profusely
between
hand-carved
frames of
unrelenting
heartbreak.

THE ABSENCE OF WONDER

Sunlight plays upon the lake,
disappears beneath the surface.

A ripple, a few air bubbles,
then nothing.

BESIDE YEWS

I have spent
all afternoon

sitting beside you,
listening to flies

buzz between us
like chainsaws.

THE HOME OF THE MUSES

...and after your hair had tumbled down the
dreams of Mount Parnassus, like a flock of

uncounted sheep, turning the
pheasant's eye green, gathering

orchids to spread like a mossy cradle onto
my misty eyes, sleepy with wine, it became

a squall of impossible memories, taking to
muscari milky blue skies above the olive groves

like a tangle of ravens.

THE ARCHER

Then, when the day has broken,
I will sit beside myself and

gather fragments of you on the
mossy bevel of the Lethe; polish

them up a little with my long-ago
soft and sleepless eyes, love and

kiss them tenderly, ordain them
each and ever summer. Fasten them

with the unflowering twine of
my keep and aim them dearly,

sorrowful, as an arrow at the sun;
and know, as I have always known,

that they will surely ride the wind
when my selfbow creaks and breaks.

**YOU WHISPERED SWEET
NOTHINGS INTO MY EAR,
WHICH DID NOT AMOUNT
TO ANYTHING, BECAME
PENITENT AND APPEALED
FOR UNDERSTANDING AND
COMPASSION. I REASSURED
YOU, WITH ALL THE FUTILITY
OF A PYRRHIC PROMISE THAT,
DESPITE YOUR BRUTAL
HISTORY OF WAR CRIMES,
I HAD NO WISH TO HANG YOU**

You offered me your portrait,
but I had covered my walls

with quadrupeds.
Characteristically

undeterred, you became
green again,

an open landscape
untrodden by sheep.

THE SEED TINDER

We were drawn to the
long days, like
supplicants eager to

be warm. Chasing
loggerheads in
leeched brooks

barefoot,
kingfishers on the
wing, hurrying

crickets home to
discover there
were ghosts in

these summers that
would not let us
gather seasons easily.

OLD AGE IS A BLOODTHIRSTY BASTARD

Old age is a
bloodthirsty bastard,
there's no such
thing as a

happy ending.
Memories turn on
you like a
pack of wolves,

searing your tongue,
so you
can't even lick
your wounds.

ANOTHER ONE OF THOSE
AWKWARD MOMENTS

It was another one of those
awkward moments and,
despite my best efforts, I just

couldn't think of anything to
say. On any other day, I
would probably have looked

earnestly sympathetic and
kept my mouth shut but,
with grieving silence

ringing out like a peal of
hammered bronze, I felt
uncomfortably mute. Then,

right out of nowhere, I over-
smiled reassuringly, and
blithely declared to his wife

that the embalmers had
made him look
the very picture of health.

A RESILIENT OPPONENT

Middle age carried an
obvious weight
advantage, shuffled

neatly and put youth
on the deck with a
stunning right hook.

Gum shield flew out,
the crowd was on its
feet. Youth beat the

count and teetered
for a moment, then
grinned back defiantly

with a full set of teeth
whiter than any
flag of surrender.

DENOUEMENT

'I am sick of
these props I have
maintained so

meticulously,'
sighed Nigel,
discarding a script;

'I have acted out
my life to critics
who were interested

in nothing but
free drinks during
the interval.'

DAWN CHORUS

On these
quiet mornings,
I like to sit in

an open field,

listening to
blackbirds pecking
songs from my flesh.

TOWARD THE ISLES OF THE BLEST

I spied you lucent with beauty,
unsettled on a precarious tide,
and caught between the
ripple and the undertow, I
could not reach as you

pulled away. But watched you,
fragile, elfin, sea spray scented,
swathed silent, tearful, dignified
in harvest moon-shadow silver
wan, as you stood, espadrilled,

halo'd beneath calico sails,
drifting downward
into calmer waters.

WHEN LOVE WAS GOLDEN

When you became too frail to fly,
I carried you inside my shirt, like
a prayer. Placed you upon a table

of oaks and held you secure amid
their branches while you learned
again to look down. Fastened you

to diminishing colours of autumn;
accompanied you beyond them, into the rain, until the fell snows came.

THE CATCHER'S TAP

The old man slept shaded on the bank of the river and dreamed of a time when he was young. In the afternoon he always slept, because the sun was too hot, and the reflected light on the water hurt his eyes. On the path, not far from the old man, walked a small boy with a butterfly cupped in the palm of his hand. As he glanced down from behind a thicket of golden curls, the small boy noticed that the old man had left the door to his soul ajar. Almost at once, the small boy released the butterfly, tapped lightly upon the door to the old man's soul, and crept in.

After an hour or two, the old man stirred, rubbed his eyes with the backs of his hands and woke from his sleep with a weight of sorrow in his soul. Despite his years, the old man did not feel old, yet his dream had troubled him, and as he caught his reflection in the water, he felt tears run down his face. 'I wish I had never been young,' he cried, as he brushed his wet cheeks, 'I could easily have borne being old if I had never been young, and my dreams tease me in the cruellest way. I am old, it is true,' wept the old man, 'and I have no heart for dreaming.'

He reclaimed his fallen hat from the dust of the river bank and watched as a butterfly opened and closed its wings on the felted head of a bulrush. 'I shall not come here to fish again,' said the old man, as he carefully replaced the hat upon a dishevelled shock of silver hair; 'I have caught a fish which I can not throw back, and I am haunted by its sorrow', he sighed, as he closed the door to his soul.

The old man left the river bank much earlier than usual and walked slowly home through the forest, stopping every so often to listen to the song of a bird, or to look up at the trees.

When he arrived at his cedar-boughed shack he was tired again, but was afraid to sleep. He stretched his frail and ancient frame over an old mattress and stared at the log wall above him. 'A wise man does not look for what he knows he can not find', he sighed, as he slowly closed his eyes.

The day was not yet over, and the old man knew that he would be asleep by nightfall. But, as he closed his eyes, he vowed that when he returned to the forest he would try to forget that he had been there before.

On the distant river bank, bulrushes whispered, mysterious, unheard in evening breezes, and some-where, deep in the old man's soul, a small boy searched for butterflies.

INVOCATION

Take me on a guided tour
of everywhere I've been before,

so I may see and then remember
how I came to be December.

CHROMATIC CONFLICT

Your sombre colour
complemented my mood,

but then my mood lightened
and we clashed badly.

WHOEVER SAID ROMANCE WAS DEAD DID NOT UNDERSTAND THE NATURE OF THE CATALEPTIC STATE

Weeping frost
spins pearl

strings on
macilent hedge-

rows, where
spectral

songbirds
spill

into the
consummating

chill of a
gradual dawn.

RAIN ANGEL

A wisp of bird-
song, airborne,

a purple sunset
kiss beneath

the spire of
evening. A

half-decanted
dirge, a

midnight choir of
yearning,

a new dawn
will not

rouse you.

YEARNING A LIVING

I collected you from
wishing wells

I threw myself into
bit by bit,

spending you on
ineffective luxuries

I could never have
otherwise indulged.

BAD COMPANY

'I'd like to be
alone with my
thoughts,' sighed
Martha,
attempting to
saturate the
colours of
a wilting bouquet,
'but I can't help
feeling that I'd
be so much
safer with
a chaperone.'

HARBOUR DAYS

Trawlers brook spent like catches beached
on sun-bleached fenders, where habitual
partners perch dockside, silent strangers to
love. Swallows weave, and children,
unchecked by possibilities, bind threads of
imagination blind to the coarse and home-
spun fabric of their garb.

Radio incidental counterpoint orchestrates
conversational preludes. Occasional invitations
parade; while the bayed racket of scavengers,
circling, greedy for the spill, fills the overmantel
grey, where old men who cannot rig the meter of
their jaunt chew another windswept cured step
toothless from their Monday morning mile.

RAPPROCHEMENT

Not even a force ten gale
could blow as many

opportunities as I have,
thought Nigel,

regretting the opportunity
he had not taken

to remove himself
from a force ten gale.

A PARAMOUR'S TORMENT: BITTER-SWEET RECOLLECTIONS OF LATENT LOGOPHILIA AND THE PAINFULLY UNEDIFYING DISSECTION OF DEFINITION

You were invariably so immaculately
presented; each syllable of your hair

chiselled filigree into the seductive
substance of sculpture. Your smile, a

ravishing repository for lipstuck,
languishing letters, your fascinator-

featured facade far ahead of the crowd.
How I would have borne catachrestic

crosses for you, served cruel and unusual
sentences to suffer being true, loved you

loquaciously with a lexicographer's lips;
if only you had not persisted as one of

those embarrassingly awkward words that
I could never quite grasp the meaning of.

THE MYTH OF EDEN

You have merited your
madness with chastening
pains, in blistering
summer fields of famine,

winters of love. You have
borne him the sallow
stripling of your favour,
witnessed the altar's tender
lean moulder and frost; the

unretiring smokestack of
your blushing nakedness
not even ripening the
petrified apple of his hand.

THE FALL OF TROY

Before it became dark, we
watched rabbits trickle down
the hillside like springwater,
wild geese fleck mandarin
suns, spilling amber into the

chenille of our shadow.
Before it became dark, we
fashioned moments into
memories which would become

too difficult to hold.
Before it became dark, we
touched each other gently when
we walked, arm in arm, like
barge mules inching the towpath.

DAFFODILS

Hawthorn fringed, this
                    scrub,
a nursery once; we
coursed contours of spiked
                    green,
circumventing flowerbeds
in scuffed shoes.

Golden brocade spanned this
                    hill;
a spring of daffodils seeped,
and we ran until blooms
                    became
empty spaces
framed by footprints.

PORTRAIT IN FADING COLOURS

I painted you
playful in bower shadow,
where Whistling Jacks grow
arboured by dusk. You
beckoned me, reclining,

clover-veiled like an
uncertain bride, from
the time when we were
younger and watched
lumpsuckers skim the millpond.

HAIKU FOR YOU
(PLUS TWO)

Your soft eyes fold closed
against the scintillant night;
sorrow bleeds through them.

Wind reads the tall grass,
the page is closed to the sun;
somewhere a plot hides.

You sleep with your back
to the wall of your darkness.
At dawn, you will dream.

THE SNOW HAS PAINTED A FLOCK OF RED-WINGS ON THE TREETOPS

I received from
you a bouquet
of uncharted

waters, gathered
unoccupied
creels of affection

in frost-tangled
mists. Valued pale
pearl moons over

South Sea tides,
mudlarked on
nugutory

promises, to
remain hamstrung
here, impoverished

among the
vagabonds of
your heart,

cursed ages
after you had
betrayed it.

MY FATHER DIED FROM ALTZHEIMER'S DISEASE

Icarus flew homeward, circling
the windsock of his bed like a

periodic breeze. I have fallen
from the warmth of the sun, he

thought, immediately noticing
that everything felt colder.

A GOSPEL OF DISAFFECTION

We cloistered ourselves
in godless supplication,

you and I,
orphans of the wind,

lost birds fluttering into
the darkness of a belief

that light had failed us.

FAWNING IN LOVE
AGAIN

Your wool is coarse as a
drunken curse, yet I wear it

next to my skin; keeps me
standing here at the font of

the brook, tending another
absent flock in the rain.

ANTIQUATED EPITAPH FOR THE BOY WHO UNWITTINGLY DRESSED EVERYBODY ELSE IN ALL THE PIECES OF HIMSELF HE THOUGHT HE HAD LOST

I watched you,
fair of face,

misplace

your last
remaining

smile,

as you
descended into

leaden

fields beneath
the fog of

Sunday's eyes.

IMPERCEPTIBLE JOURNEYS: THE UNSCALABLE CONSUMMATION OF BELIEF

We were tourists then. Sightseers. Backpacking
our spring kisses and trespassing touches;
promenading countercurrents on dreamdrifting
tides; impeccable pearls in our shell. We were

wordless waders in amniotic streams, embryonic
amblers. Unvaned nestlings beneath treecreeping
stars. Silk-skinned ripplers, catchers and pitchers
of winged and nimble smiles. We were bleeding:

runnels of province into each other's unwrought
scars. Brittling our bones in the monolithic shadow
of our union. Mislaying familiar contours of our
faces among the settlers who occupied them, we

were destitute. Impoverished by the extravagance
of baptismal re-immersion. Owning little but a fear
of loss; hawking souvenir wounds for crumbs in
a thousand spectral countries of ever-golden mists.

EPILOGUE

Seasons have reduced
you to winter; dark,
flameless,

ringed, like ancient
timber, sad-
eyed;

cradling my smile
as if it were
your own child.

THE QUESTION

The small boy wandered into a shady copse of doubt and wrestled with problems he could not resolve. As he knelt down to look more closely at an unusual flower, he suddenly noticed that the flower had disappeared, and in its place he was surprised to see a grey toad. He continued his descent onto the soft ground, and was about to stroke the toad with an outstretched finger when the toad immediately changed into a young lamb. Amazed and delighted, the small boy stroked the young lamb joyfully, ruffling its soft, curly coat, until it let out a fearful roar and at once changed into a bear. The small boy jumped to his feet in terror.

'Don't be afraid', said the bear.

'But you could harm me!' uttered the small boy, nervously.

'I could, indeed. And sometimes you will meet me and regret it. But not today.'

'Who are you?' the small boy asked, almost too afraid to move.

'I am truth', replied the bear, drawing himself up onto his hind legs, looking twice as tall and even more fearsome.

'But you change so quickly and easily,' cried the small boy, awed and shadowed by the bears' huge, upright frame,

'how shall I know it is you if I meet you again?'
'That,' riddled the bear, changing into a cloud and
floating away, 'is something that only your own
questions will be able to answer.'

A PASSIONATE CONFLICT
OF CONVICTIONS

Was it true for you that the
maimed were best practised

in the arts of love?

Or was veracity a necessary
delusion? because, like all the

other women of Themiscyra,

you held the rule of your breast
so much cheaper than war?

A TENTATIVE SUPPLICATION

The curious thing about your faith

is

how you insinuate your devotion;

surreptitiously

rubbing your hands together in

adjuration,

as though warming them from the cold.

THE IDIOT

When I was
younger, I
used to play
the idiot.

Now that I
am older,
I don't need
to play
quite so hard.

CHILDHOOD

Childhood is a cemetery of unmarked graves,
unknown soldiers unarmed,
cut down in the conflict of
a life lived in moments.

Childhood is the father of the sole survivor,
the bearer of the ruined flag,
the weeper for a fallen army.
The western scud master of the

Slate brume dripping over charcoal fields of
smouldering summers, like
lovesick tears raining
salty in the crowlight.

FAVOURITE STREET

Back on Favourite Street,
don't need a crutch;

walking discretely in
a milling crowd

almost disguises
my limp.

THE SCREAM

'I have arrived at
the end of my
ability to

speak without
repeating myself',
cried Martha,

hollering into a
canyon of
distress; refreshing

the chorus of
her echo over
and over again.

ISLANDS

I mislaid a trail
of return when

my teardrops
dried; calcifying

into vegetative
islands I could

never quite
sail away from.

ON THE BENT KNEED, BROKEN, IOPTEROUS DAWN, I PLUNGED WITH A RELUCTANT SYMPHONY OF OUTSTRETCHED ARMS FLAPPING AND WAVING FROM THE PRECARIOUS LEDGE OF DREAMS TO THE DUBIOUS INFIRMARY OF YOUR NETTLED EMBRACE

Night died in regrettable circumstances.
The critical casualty breathing its last in

pitfall traps of ratiocination insidiously
shovelled between unilluminated paths

of modified pronouncements and truths;
inevitably having drunkenly succumbed

to the paralysing poison of putative pre-
cepts it had been assiduously compelled

to consume. We carried the body home,
purifying it with fresh, clean, reassuring

promises erupting like diatribes from
amputated arteries of trust. Knowing,

by the conventional discomfort of
performing such elucidating rituals

that, without the ink of a familiar
darkness, we would never find the

consolation of another dream un-
troubled enough to sleep through.

THE INEVITABLE CATASTROPHE OF INTERPRETATION BEGETS THE UN-NATURAL BASTARD BIRTH OF DISILLUSION

Wounded in crossfire reverie as the sun fell
masquerading as sleep; waking, faith-parched,
shaken, breathless to discover the bleating
dreaming blind. Invoking reassurance from
solemn psalms of abbreviated glances,
crouching in such shallow phrases, our
thoughts could not pose naked for the night.

Threading ritual sophist spangle onto star-split
drapery of deception, frostwoodsandled, scalpel-
cold. Bluff-carved, hunkering anxious beneath a
cherry-minted thirty pieces of browblood
burnished silver moon, swollen, easeled between
shivering beech ale-amber thighs painting our
shadowy figures newborn soft, unseasoned by sun,
cadaverous strains of arpeggiated evening pallor.

THE KISS

I want to live
long enough to
enjoy my death,

to offer it the
hospitality of a
convivial host, to

embrace it, tenderly,
like a woman
I have always loved.

THE TRANSIENCE OF ETERNAL LOVE

What matters is the
way you

touch my hand

when you tell me
how

Iliona seized Polymestor's eyes;

sinking your fingernails
further and

further into my flesh,

as if to motion the
reassurance

that you could

never be so moved
to hurt me.

THE SPIRAL PAINTER

Now I wait for you in altered oils,
framed, unframed, a little dark and
rubbed around the edges; dressed

undressed, I caress you with the
edge of my finger.

Now I animate you in Arcadian
reflections; colour still holds me,
neither of us is lost.

Now I retouch everything. The
stammer, the sough, the bits no-

one else can see; beyond the
yellow varnish of the
horizon, the impossible sky.

**I MERELY SUGGESTED
THAT BEFORE YOU
ATTEMPTED TO TAKE
THE SPLINTER OUT OF
MY EYE YOU SHOULD
REMOVE THE PLANK
FROM YOUR OWN.
THIS YOU OBLIGINGLY
DID AND PROMPTLY
BLUDGEONED ME INTO
SUBMISSION WITH IT**

I lost you on the ebb-
tide, with the soft sand of

tender words still clinging to an
amusement arcade at the end of

the old pier of pretending that
neither of us would ever take

so readily to the sea.

THIRTY DEGREES OF FROST HAD CAUSED THE BLOOD TO FREEZE IN HER VEINS

Little by little, she lost
her voice in the wind.

She called and called
until all she could hear

was the night cracking
like kindling behind her.

LOVE LESSEN

Love is
biting your

tongue when

another's tongue has
bitten you.

Turning another

cheek when
another's cheek

has turned on

you. Love means
never having to

say you're sorry;

because you've
already said it a

thousand times

and you can't say
how sorry you are

for having repeated
yourself

so often.

THE WEIGH IN

He looked life in
the eye but
life stared him

down; you could
tell right away
that it was

never going to be
an evenly matched
encounter.

STILL LIFE
WITH
GOLDENROD
AND
NIGHTSHADE

The leaden
lexicon of
your

kiss was
never more
than

skin. An inutile
bridge that
could never

span such a
detachment of
meaning.

AMBUSH

Sometimes death strikes as a
marching band, sometimes

shoeless, silent as secrets. Sometimes the artful keep an ear to

the ground, taken unawares
whilst listening for footsteps.

TRUMPETER
OF
MORNING

Undimmed,
unlit,
I return
bedraggled to
your beach,
driftwood
blown in
from
the lee.

REPORTING FOR DUTY

The small boy's father dreamed of the sea,
like a lover dreams of the scent of skin. It didn't
matter which sea; any would do. He needed to

escape. The small boy never dreamed of the
sea. Mostly, he dreamed of his father and
of being a father like him. One

day, the small boy watched his father wake
from a customary short summer Sunday afternoon siesta, and soon after, quietly asked:

'What did you dream, Father?'
His father looked kindly at the small boy and
answered unhesitatingly:

'I always dream of you, my son', he purred,
folding corners of the morning newspaper
into a sailboat.

THE INSOLUBLE HARMONIES OF COLOUR

The old man sat down against a stump of reflection and began to strip the bark from his torment with a sharp intake of breath.

'I have,' he thought, 'always expected my dour palette to yield a colour bright enough to lead me, with no consideration of the canvas to which I may have applied it. My brushes were the rocks of my ignorance, which I did not learn to use with delicacy, and my pigment I hid jealously beneath my contempt for the opinions of others. Now I am alone, and my paint has hardened beyond use.' As he softly easeled his head on hands tangled like the knuckled roots of an ancient tree, he heard a chorus of sheep bleating a ruminating song while they ambled slowly towards him.

The old man recognised the song at once, and raised his gaze to meet the bearded face of a venerable bellwether. 'It's a simple song', offered the bellwether, as a greeting, with a smile. 'We chew, we sleep, we sing, we amble. The colours of our life are few and muted.'

'Yet you paint so beautifully with them,' replied the old man, moved and quieted by the unaffected honesty of the ram, 'I could not match your mastery.'

'We paint what we are able, old man, we make no study of our inability. Our song does not alter with expectation.'

'Even so, do you never wish for more than you have?' asked the old man, keenly, trying for a moment to comprehend the absence of desire.

'More suns? More grass? More sleep? More song? How would we profit from such a wish, or even the hope that such a wish may be granted?' shrugged the bellwether, with a cordial chuckle.

'I have always wished for more,' sighed the old man, apologetically, 'my life has been spent in the pursuit of a formula which would multiply my desires and secure my success. I realise now that my efforts have been wasted. I have not in all my searching found the words to my song.' The bellwether evaluated the old man's lament pensively and attempted to fathom the nagging root of his anguish.

'We are sheep,' he began, following a few moments of puzzled head-scratching and another good natured shrug, 'we have no comprehension of your complaint.'

'My compunction is simple. I am a man, and as all men, I burned with the desire to succeed. To be better than all other men, to confront my peers with my finery, to arm myself with riches, to cultivate envy among my fellows.'

'To what purpose?' begged the baffled ram.

The old man let loose a long sigh and looked hard into a hazy distance for a reply.

'To be accepted,' he mused, at last, 'to be recognised as one of my flock. To follow what was expected of me; to be an example of conformity and to sing a song which everybody knew.'

'You are too clever for me, old man. We sheep are uncomplicated beasts; we greet the sun in the morning, meander over meadows in song, chew the sweet clover and frolic in silvery streams. If we were intelligent animals, maybe we, too, would cultivate desires and strive for success, but as it is, we can only marvel at the strange magic of your words and carry on singing.'

And as the swelling sun shone like saffron on watery hills, the old man searched the stretched and pine-selvedged sky-line for a cooling shower of unformed replies, while the bellwether ambled away with his bleating number toward a fresh green pasture, chewing and frolicking and singing the same song they had always sung.

THE GHOST DANCE

In the morning, I folded your
shadow into a companionable

hollow on my pillow, inhaled
the corsage of your hair, a

spring of imperishable perfume;
idled in the arpeggiated piano of

your awakening; memorialised
a repertoire of duets from an

era when improvising such
music was easy, like listening to

Sidney Bechet in the summer
afternoon sun of your fingers.

REMEMBRANCE

There are shapes in this sand no
tide will fill, nor any breeze blow
nameless into night. In celandine

fetches aside bygone pathways;
between nightjar, corncrake over
cuckoo flower cries, countered

by the bellow of a quarter master
moon spilling like a thistle in the
blister of the distance between us.

CAESARIAN MORNING

And there you were, as
though you had always

been. Ingenuous,
immaculate. Rosy-

pink and bloody from
sleep; tumultuously

torn from the
gaping belly of night.

A DECORATIVE DISCOURSE

For a peppercorn rent, we

continued to occupy those

confined spaces between us, where

the furniture of our differences

had become so painfully comfortable.

VERNAL ODE

Oh, spring;
sweet scent of

putrefying winter,

I lie enraptured on
your bed of bulbs,

a hungry leper

ravished by
a nun.

THE GAINING OF WISDOM

By the time I was five, my
family had already become
ravens and spent most of

their free time languishing
atop telegraph poles. In the
winter of '75, my sister was

ruined by a whaling harpoon
as she perched on a bird table
and my mother forgot how to

speak. I was seventeen when
I lost my hair and acquired a
taste for ritualistic yearning.

But when my grandfather
refused to consume the
nourishment of human

desires, I realised that all
birds ultimately succumb to
the need of the superstitious

to suffer; so, I retired from my
pursuit of the obvious to a
small patch of briar, where

I now perch, filleting
intractable regrets
beneath a mackerel sky.

A COMPLEX ABSOLUTION - THE PROTRACTED GEOMETRY OF FORGIVENESS

It was not so large an area,
the circumference of our

circle. It was only in the
drawing of it that we

could not decide precisely
where the line should be

permitted to join.

SIMPLE TRANSMUTATION

We were never quite
meticulous enough to

surmount the predicament of
communicating ingenuously.

Somehow, it was invariably
more expedient to occupy end-

less evenings deconstructing
unsophisticated questions

to form impossibly
complicated replies.

THE THUNDER
BEARER

Sweat upon sweat, from
incipient dawn to
strolling homeward over
varicose veins of

purple hill's
night-furrowed brow.
Blood spill sky
drips like

brushes on tympani,
heather underfoot,
counterpoint, arousing

choruses of
contemplation, and
two black dogs in my
satchel; both hungry.

THE LONG DAY HAS FALLEN TO THE HORIZON

The long day has fallen to the horizon, a
lame nag arrowed in the homeward canter. The
moribund quarry, grotesque in its capitulation,
a bloody mount struck riderless into the scar.
(Disingenuous sightseers gawp, vulgar, at the

pre-carved spectacle of the withering mundane,
stand awe-struck by their inability to dog-ear the
page. Caught between the sentence and the
meaning, they punctuate the passage with
grunts of ignorance.)

The long day has fallen to the horizon, fettered
by loss to the stain of disgrace. Urchins huddle
chilled beneath a storm petrel sky, where a
whip-crack moonless wind blows their
seedless husk chalk-dust fledgling footprints
into the Christ-hungry dark.

SCHRÖDINGER'S CATASTROPHE: THE DOGGED PERSISTENCE OF DILEMMA

This perpetual agony of
breath somehow always

compels me to breathe.

Such insistence on
belief leaves me

broken with desire.

Such untamed aversion to
certainty curses me over

and over with the hope

that even you could soon be
light enough to be warm.

RESTRICTED VIEW

There were times when
we felt we had
succeeded, others when

we thought we had failed.
Occasionally, we
were unable to ascertain

exactly how we had fared.
Mostly, we concluded
that the possible was

an ill-determined
area which could
not be charted accurately.

THE WORK ETHIC

'Pain is not a thing I am
comfortable with,' thought
Nigel, as he nailed his

ankle to the trunk of
a beech tree, 'but I
would rather do something

useful than feel that I have
completely wasted yet
another precious day.'

THE SHADOW

The small boy glanced behind him and
noticed there was darkness.
'There is something dark behind me, Father',
he exclaimed, in a measure of surprise.
'It is your shadow', replied the old man, tenderly.
'Will it harm me?' asked the small boy, anxiously.
The old man watched, smiling, as the small boy
attempted to disengage himself from his unyielding
appendage.
'That will depend,' the old man advised, after a
few moments of quiet amusement, 'on where you
allow it to fall.'

ANGLE OF REPOSE

The old man draped a limp arm
around a shoulder of solitude,

marrying a melting memory to
the moon. 'Another day has

flown my nest', he sighed,
plucking elusive souvenirs from

illuminated nurseries of nightfall.

ANOTHER BEAU TO YOUR STRING

Ah, how you reeled him in, dripping with
morning, green and lush. How you stole

him from his fields of corn, plucked hollow
the orchard of his eyes. Fed him to the

famished cane of your command. Lost him
in your ramshackle coterie of tumbledown days.

FROM THE NIGHT
GARDEN

We were only ever
children of the old;

shifting as wishes,
swollen bellied,

thirsty for
songs of the rain.

We lingered there
until the river had

spoken; our kisses
growing hard and

sinewy as the wind.

SYMPHONY

Thunder plays a piano
piece for left
hand, cello storms after

woodwind in a penguin
suit sky. Moonlight
intermezzo melts into

first quiet chords of
daybreak, shimmering
like young leaves on

branches arced with rain.

APRIL SARABANDE

We two-stepped in the
shadow of the wrecking

ball, photographing the
dance hall with a confessional

eye; tossing the timber caber of a
chance remark into the weeping

wish that we had retained
just one splinter in the palm.

TUIST REPLY

You speak my words
so beautifully,
you make me wish
that I had
thought of them.

SHIVER

In winter, I
feel like a
stranger;
retracing footprints
I can not remember
leaving.

POSSUM RISING

'Who the hell do I
think I'm kidding,'
thought Nigel,

kicking himself
sharply in
a sensitive moment;

'It is becoming
increasingly
obvious that my

gift for playing dead
has been completely
wasted on this life.'

THE CLOSING OF SUMMER

Through the roundel, the
wild goose wades out of

frame. Camera pans.
Weeping anguish dresses

the stage in ash. Beneath
a blinding sun

the air is black with the
smoke of lovers.

SOMEBODY SOMEWHERE
IS DYING TO BE BORN

Bring on your muscle of morning,
pit your imperious fist against

mine; I stared down the night I
was afraid of,

and it was darker than you.

SEPIA ROADS

We are no longer
able
to brush away
tears
which have etched
themselves
into fleshlines. Nor

load the bristle
with the
brilliant tones of
our first
embrace. Now that
the oaks have
grown,

we stand
a little smaller in
their shade,
fumbling for
each other's
hand, overpainting
deeper sepia roads.

SHORT CHAPTERS
FROM SUNSET

Day kisses a rose onto
twilight's face

from

the blooming garden of
its ember,

scenting

darkening skin a sweet
snare for

gullible

drifters on the
wing.